Steve
Rosenberg

Recorder Playing

Fingering chart

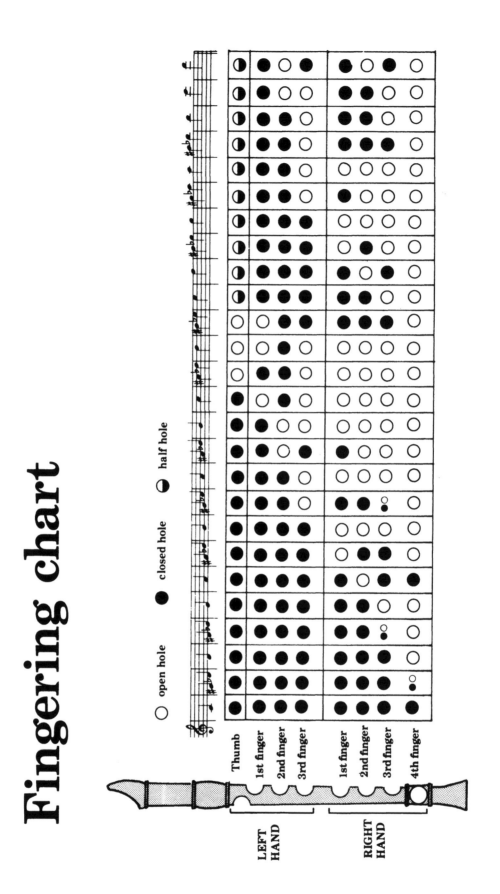

Recorder Playing

Introduction

In recent years there has been a tremendous resurgence of interest in early music. The recorder has always played a central role in this music, so that it seems fitting to me that we should use it in schools where the recorder is taught. I have, therefore, made considerable use of this authentic music for the recorder; music of the renaissance and baroque periods, which were the golden eras for the instrument, and I am sure that this music will both delight and inspire the student to go further with his or her musical studies. I have also included many duets and trios so that even at this early level the pupils will start making music in groups. It is my hope that this book will improve the status of the recorder in today's schools.

I am greatly indebted to Roger Buckton, Alec Loretto and to my colleagues at the North Shore Teachers College, who have taken such a helpful and constructive interest in this method, through all its long formative stages.

To the Teacher

The recorder is an ideal classroom instrument. After only a few lessons the pupil is starting to play real music, giving a feeling of interest and genuine achievement almost at once. It is also a serious musical instrument with a rich and varied repertoire, and it is my experience that an understanding of the instrument is arrived at much more quickly if appropriate music is used from the very beginning.

The teacher will find the following suggestions helpful:

1. Playing by ear (echo playing) should be an integral part of your lessons. The teacher should invent simple one or two bar phrases and have the class play them back.
2. Do not go on until the class has grasped each lesson.
3. At the beginning of each lesson practice the new note, holding it with a long steady breath.
4. Add percussion accompaniments to the pieces wherever you wish.
5. Each new piece should be read as slowly as possible so that there can be careful attention to detail. Then, work up to the tempo that suits the whole class. Metronome marks and tempo indications have deliberately been avoided, partly because they would be anachronistic in this music, but also to encourage a creative and thoughtful approach to the music.
6. When working on the duets and trios all pupils should learn all the parts.
7. Most important of all, I hope the class will enjoy their recorder playing.

Auckland 1976   Steve Rosenberg

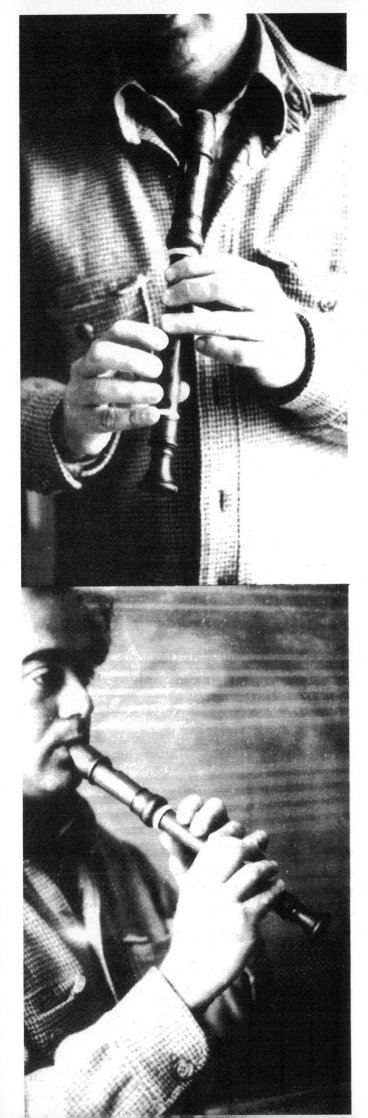

Holding the Recorder

The recorder is held with the left hand at the upper half of the instrument and placed so that the thumb can easily close the thumb hole at the back. The first three fingers of the left hand cover the top three holes of the recorder.

The thumb of the right hand supports the recorder underneath, and the little finger of the right hand helps to support and steady the recorder by being positioned between the two lower double holes. The first, second and third fingers will now be in the right position to cover their holes when we reach these notes.

Breathing

Take the instrument to your mouth and place the mouthpiece between the lips in such a way that the mouthpiece remains dry. Breathe deeply without raising your shoulders, filling the lower part of your lungs. Do not *blow* into the recorder, but *breathe* into it, as though you were warming your hands with your breath. Do not blow from the throat.

Tonguing

Each note must begin with a tongue movement. The tongue is placed on the roof of your mouth just behind the upper front teeth, and you then pronounce the syllable **"du"**.

B

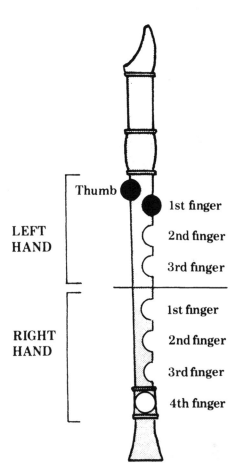

Starting to Play

To play your first note (B) finger the recorder as shown in the diagram with the first finger and thumb of the left hand covering their holes, and tongue the syllable **"du"**.

Cover the holes so that they are completely sealed. If you breathe too hard into the recorder the note will shriek.

The sign $\frac{4}{4}$ means that there are four crotchet (quarter note) ♩ beats in each bar. The top figure always tells how many beats to count, and the lower figure tells us what sort of note is the counting unit.

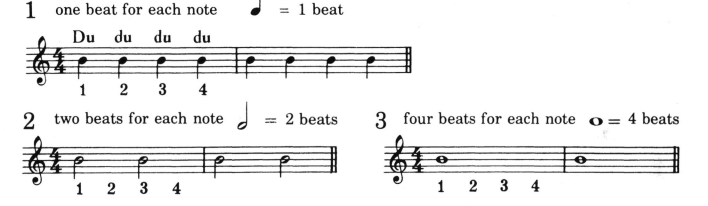

1 one beat for each note   ♩ = 1 beat

Du du du du
1 2 3 4

2 two beats for each note   ♩ = 2 beats
1 2 3 4

3 four beats for each note   o = 4 beats
1 2 3 4

When you see this sign: ✓ you should take a quick quiet breath, breathing through the mouth.

Play each line with a steady beat and without interruption.

4

Aim for a clear and beautiful sound.

5

A

6 You now have two fingers and your thumb covering the holes.

7 The holes must be covered completely, as the slightest gap will distort the note.

8 The tongue and fingers should work together: tongue the note at exactly the same time that your finger moves on or off the hole.

9

10 Always keep a steady beat. Learn each piece very slowly at first.

11 Remember each note must be tongued.

G

12 Now there are three holes covered plus the thumb. You must be careful that all are completely sealed.

13 Keep your fingers relaxed.

14

15

1 2   1 2   1 2

Count two to a bar.

16 A tune with the first three notes

The important things to remember are:

1. Breathe from the lower part of your lungs.
2. Breathe gently into the recorder.
3. Tongue each note with "**du**".

17 The Palace Steps

Practice the pieces until you know them well. Do not go on until you can play each one with ease.

A new time signature ¾

All the pieces so far have had either two or four beats to the bar; there is also a lot of music which has three beats to a bar. The first beat is stronger than beats two and three.

♩ = one beat   ♩ = two beats   ♩. = three beats;

18 a dot after a note increased the length of a note by half its original duration.

19 The dots inside a double bar show that that section must be repeated.

20

With these three notes you are now able to play many tunes. You might wish to add a percussion part to these pieces.

21 The Shepherd's Tune

When you go from G to B take care that you lift both fingers at the same time.

22 Ponsonby

23 A BAG of Joy

C

24 Now the thumb and second finger of the left hand are covering the holes. The other fingers should not be too high.

25 To go from **A** to **C** all you do is lift the first finger.
Do not lift your fingers too high.

26

27 Alman

SUSATO (16th century)

Always think about:
    Breathing
    Tonguing

The fingerings you will be able to learn quickly, but you must also always aim for a beautiful sound.

28 Exercise

When moving from C to B make sure that the first finger comes down exactly as the second finger is raised.

D

29 This is the first time that you are not using your left hand thumb.
This note does not need too much breath pressure.

30 To go from C to D just lift your thumb. Do not forget to tongue each note (**du**).

31 To support the recorder securely make sure that the thumb and little finger of the right hand are holding the instrument.

32 Duet

When playing the duets in class each part should be played by half the class, and then switched round. Have fun with the duets. Learn the parts thoroughly.

With these five notes you have learnt you are on your way to discovering the world of music. It is important not to go fast, but learn everything completely before going on.

33

For classroom use, try improvising a percussion accompaniment to the pieces.

34

Quavers / eighth notes

Quavers (eighth notes) are written like this: ♪ two or more like this: ♫

They are half as long as a crotchet (quarter note). To count them divide the beat into two parts and imagine the word "and" on the second part.

35

1 2 3 4   1 and 2 and 3 and 4 and   1 2 3 4

1 2 and 3 4 and

36

37 Dance

Michael PRAETORIUS
1571 - 1621

These pieces were written when the recorder was in its "Golden Age". This
music has become very popular again today and recorder players all over the
world play these early pieces which are part of the recorder's repertoire.

38

39 Burgundian dance

Claude GERVAISE (16th century)

Rests

As well as the written notes, music also has rests (silences), which are measured in the same way as the notes.

	NOTE	REST	
Semibreve (whole note)			4 beats (counts)
Minim (half note)			2 beats
Crotchet (quarter note)			1 beat

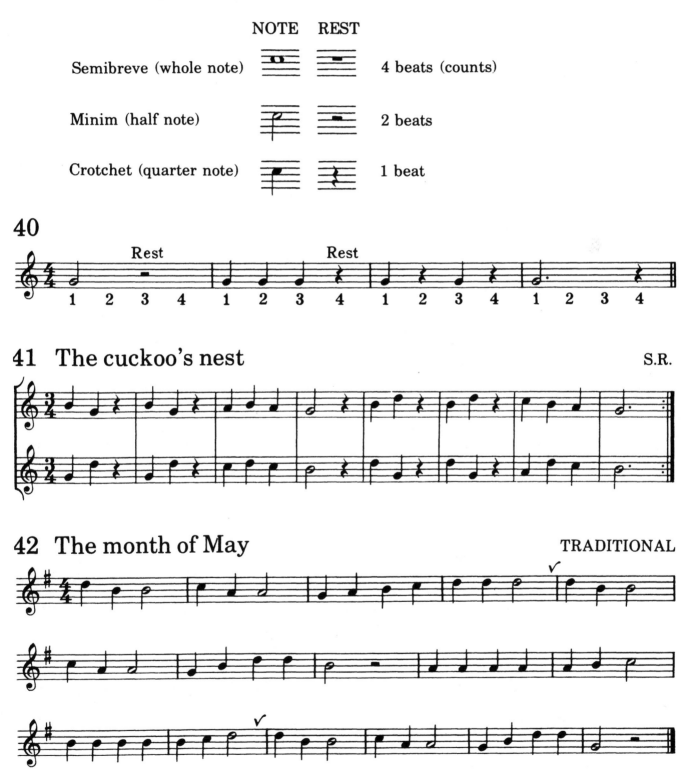

40

41 The cuckoo's nest

S.R.

42 The month of May

TRADITIONAL

Review pages

You have now learnt five notes. Before going on to the next note make sure that you can play these five notes correctly.

On these two review pages there are some finger exercises using all the notes learnt so far, and two canons.

43

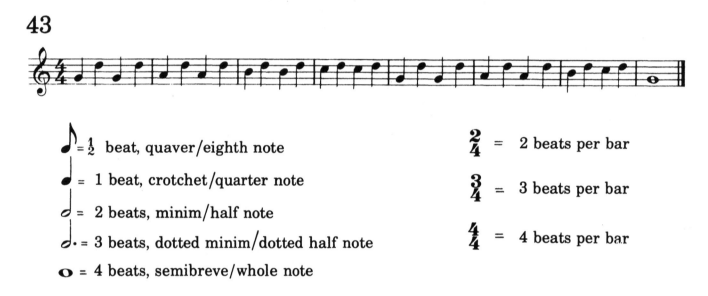

♪ = ½ beat, quaver/eighth note

♩ = 1 beat, crotchet/quarter note

𝅗𝅥 = 2 beats, minim/half note

𝅗𝅥. = 3 beats, dotted minim/dotted half note

𝅝 = 4 beats, semibreve/whole note

$\frac{2}{4}$ = 2 beats per bar

$\frac{3}{4}$ = 3 beats per bar

$\frac{4}{4}$ = 4 beats per bar

44

45

46

47 Two Canons

David MENZIES

48

F#(sharp)

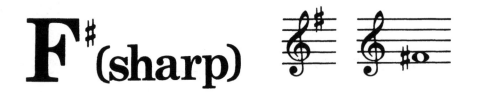

For the first time you will be using your right hand fingers. To learn the note finger a G, and then add the second and third fingers of your right hand.

The sign for a sharp is written like this ♯ , and it makes the note one semi-tone higher. If it is written just after the clef it is called a key signature and it will then apply to all the notes of that pitch in the piece. If it is written before a particular note in the piece, it then only applies to notes of that pitch in that bar.

49

50 To go from G to F sharp add fingers 2 and 3 of the right hand.

51 Noël

Esprit Philippe CHEDEVILLE
1696 - 1762

52 Dance

HAUSMANN
16th century

53 Allemande

SUSATO

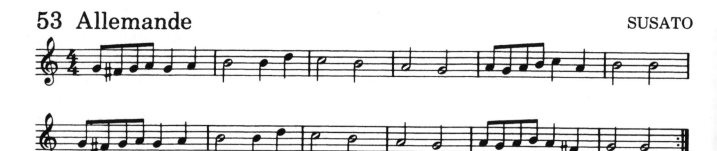

14

E

Close all the left hand holes and put down your first two right hand fingers. The lower notes do not need as much breath pressure as the higher notes.

54

Be careful not to overblow (blow too hard) on the low notes.

55

56 A song for you

S.R.

Tongue gently and play this piece sweetly, after all, I wrote it for you.

57 There was a pretty lass

ANON. (17th century)

Keep a steady beat. Don't play this piece too fast. Practice carefully, and remember that the more you practice the better you will play.

D

58 Another low note. Start by playing E, and then add your third finger of the right hand. Tongue with the **du** syllable. It may take a bit of practice to seal all the notes completely.

59 Be careful that all the holes are completely covered and that each note is tongued gently.

60 Canon

Thomas TALLIS
1505 - 1585

61 Exercise

Do not lift the right hand fingers too high, and keep them exactly over the holes which they cover.

62 Bourée

Espirit Philippe CHEDEVILLE

63 Bransle

GERVAISE

Tied notes

A curved line joining two consecutive notes of the same pitch is called a tie. Do not tongue the second of the two notes; it must sound like one continuous note.

64

65

Here are two ways of writing the same passage:

66

Once again, two ways of writing the same passage:

67

68 Trolly Lolly

William CORNISH
1465 - 1523

69 Sicilian dance

Lupi di CARRAGGIO
1607

70 Bransle

GERVAISE

71 Noël

Espirit Philippe CHEDEVILLE

19

F

Look at the fingering carefully. Many lazy players forget to place the right hand little finger down, and poor tuning results.

72 All the fingers are down except the middle finger of the right hand.

73 You will have to practice hard to play with the little finger down.

74 Canon

75 Dance

SUSATO

Tongue very gently.

B♭ (flat)

The thumb and fingers one and three of the left hand are covering the holes. The first finger of the right hand is also down.

The sign for a flat is written like this ♭ , and it makes the note one semitone lower. If it is written just after the clef it is called a key signature and it will then apply to all the notes of that pitch in the piece. If it is written before a particular note in the piece, it then only applies to notes of that pitch in that bar.

78 La Parma PHALESE 16th century

79 Dance from Champagne GERVAISE

Second Review

You have now learnt ten notes. Here is a review page of exercises, and a "Trumpet Tune" by the famous composer Henry Purcell.

80 F sharp Exercise

81 E Exercise

82 D Exercise

83 F Exercise

84 B flat Exercise

85 Trumpet tune

Henry PURCELL
1659-1695

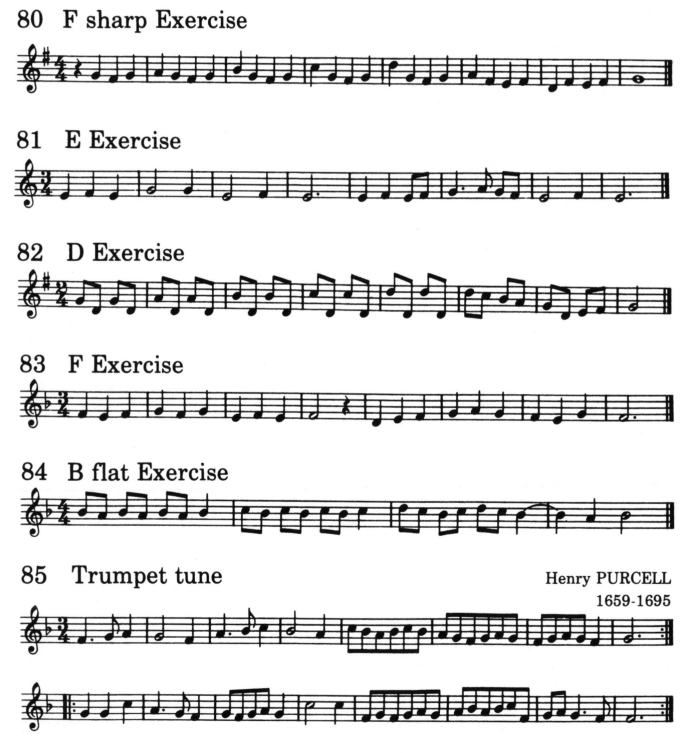

E

Finger the low E and play the note. Now for the high E the fingering is exactly the same except that you have to allow for a slight gap at the thumb hole. This is done by bending the thumb at the joint so that the thumb nail enters the hole, and only a small portion of the hole remains open. We call this pinching.

86

pinch   pinch

87

88 Exercise

89 La Bergamasca

TRADITIONAL 16th century

90 Suite

Jacques HOTTETERRE

Hotteterre was a famous instrument maker, composer and woodwind player in France. This suite was written for the recorder about 1700.

I DANCE

II MINUET 1

III MINUET 2

91 Allemande

GERVAISE

Compound time $\frac{6}{8}$

γ $\flat$ quaver (eighth notes)

ξ $\downarrow$ crotchet (quarter notes)

ξ. $\downarrow$.   dotted crotchet

When the beat note is divided equally into three parts we use a dotted note for one beat and call this compound time. In $\frac{6}{8}$ time there are two dotted crotchet (quarter) beats in each bar. These beats divide equally into three quavers (eighths).

92

1 2 3 4 5 6 1 2 3 4 5 6 1 2 3 4 5 6 1 2 3 4 5 6
1   2   1   2   1   2   1   2

93

94 Rondo

Jacques HOTTETERRE

95 Ductia

ANON. 13th century

25

C

The lowest note. All the fingers are covering the holes. Learn the note by fingering and playing the low D and then adding the little finger of the right hand.

Tongue the note very gently. Very little breath pressure is needed for this note.

If your recorder is in three pieces, the lower joint should be turned so that it corresponds to where the little finger falls naturally.

96

Du

97 La Bergamasca

TRADITIONAL 16th century

98 Exercise

99 Under the Linden Tree

ANON. 16th century

100 Rigaudon

Jacques HOTTETERRE

101 C major scale

102 Paules Wharfe

103 Nonesuch

PLAYFORD
1650

High **F**

Play the low F. Now remove the right hand little finger, pinch the thumb hole, and you are playing high F.

104

The little finger is down for the lower octave and removed for the high octave.

105

106 The Village Dance

Michael PRAETORIUS

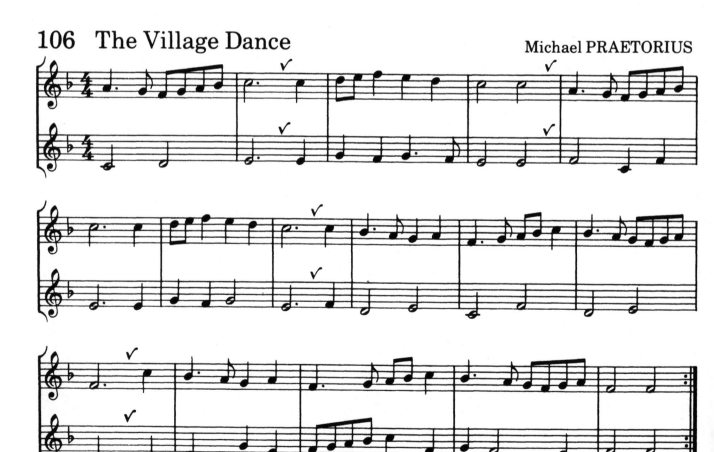

107 Sumer is icumen in (canon)

Sumer is icumen in is the earliest known canon, it is thought to have been written in about 1226 at Reading Abbey in England. It can be played by four recorders, each new part entering when the part before it has reached the asterisk, i.e. at two bar intervals.

108 Burgundian Bransle

Michael PRAETORIUS
16th century

High **G**

The higher octave will require more breath pressure than the lower.

Finger exactly like the low G, except for the pinched thumb hole.

109

110

111 Aria

Georg Philipp TELEMANN
1681 - 1767

This piece should be played fairly quickly, breathing only at the double bars.

112 Minuet

Jacques HOTTETERRE

113 La Dubois

DE LAVIGNE

114 Rondeau

Jacques HOTTETERRE

115 The old man

ANON. 16th century

Contents